Bastien Piano Basics

PERFORMANCE
LEVEL 2

BY JANE SMISOR BASTIEN

Contents

*To reinforce the feeling of achievement, the teacher or student may put a √ when the page has been mastered.

ISBN 0-8497-5276-0

2

Old West Rodeo

Use with pages 4-6 of Piano, *Level 2.*

4

Fish Scales

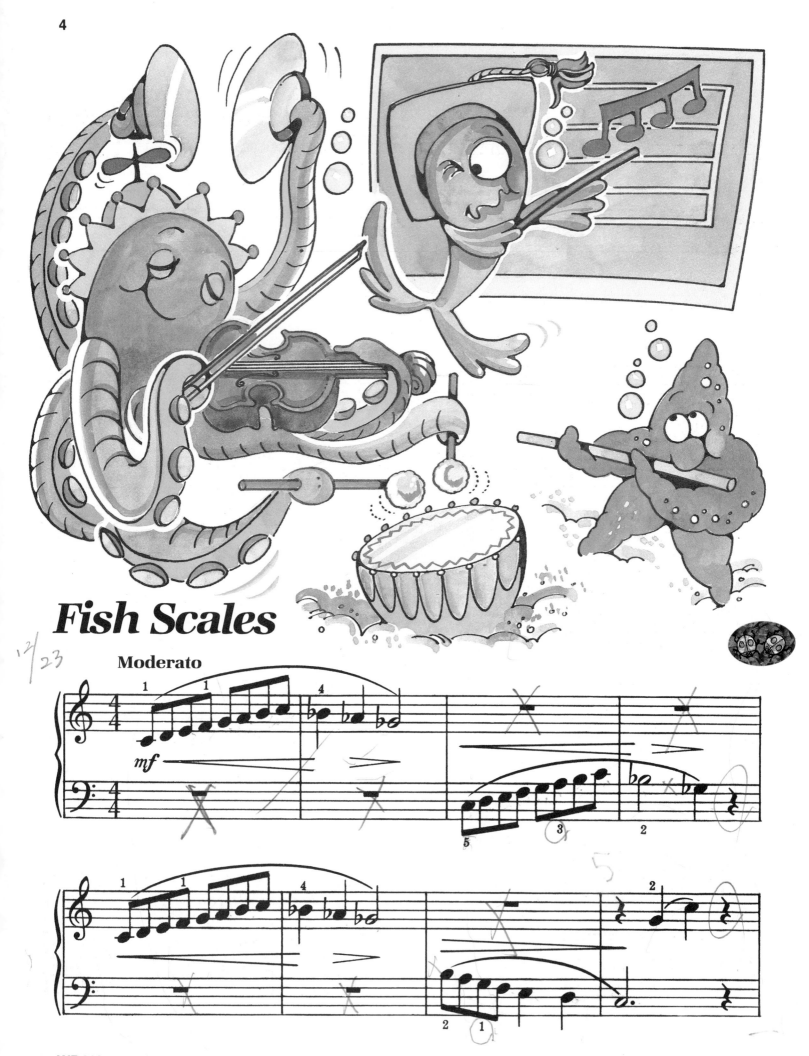

12/23

Moderato

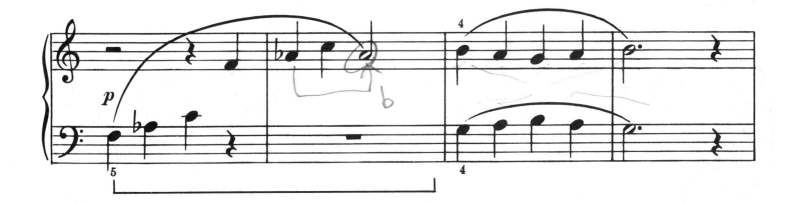

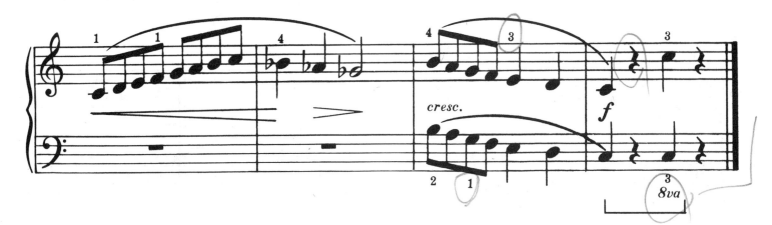

6

Springtime

Allegretto

Electronic Game

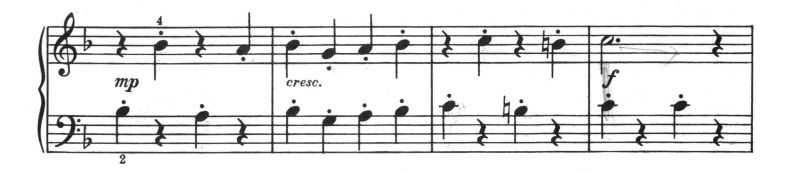

Comin' Round the Mountain

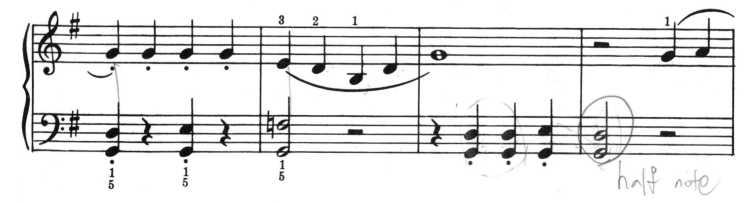

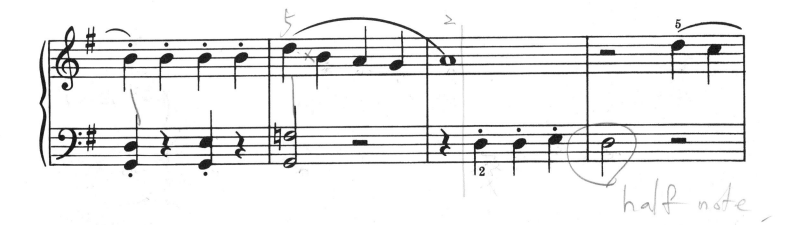

half note

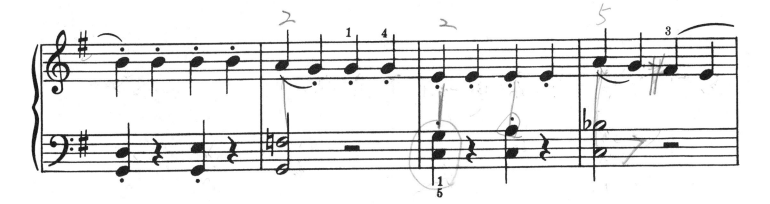

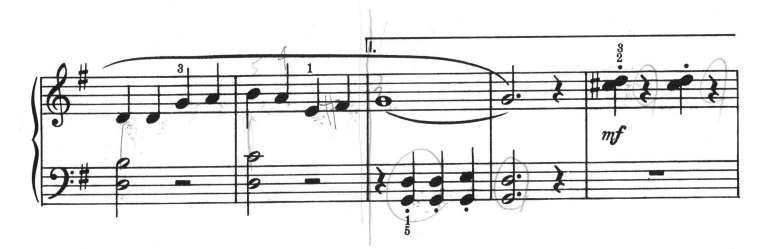

Rocket Boogie

Fast boogie beat

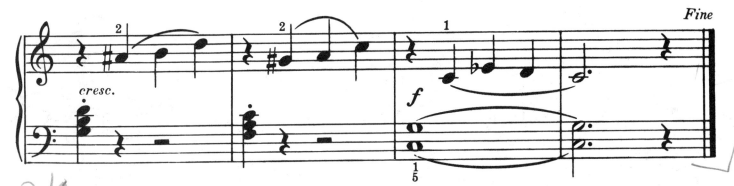

Flying high!

© DISNEY

The Golden Gate Bridge

Moderato

3/13

mf Look out the win - dow and what do I see? The

Gold - en Gate Bridge, plain as can be. I'm

in San Fran - cis - co I'm sure you can tell, The

Fine

Gold - en Gate   bridge you must   know ver - y   well.

(D. C.) al Fine

The Water Slide

3/25.

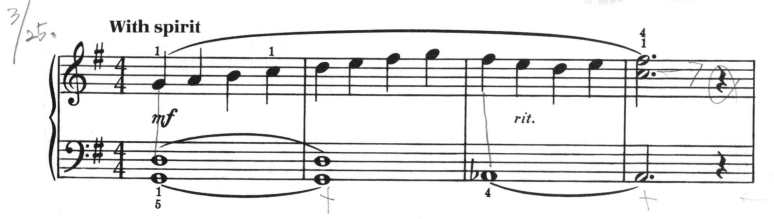

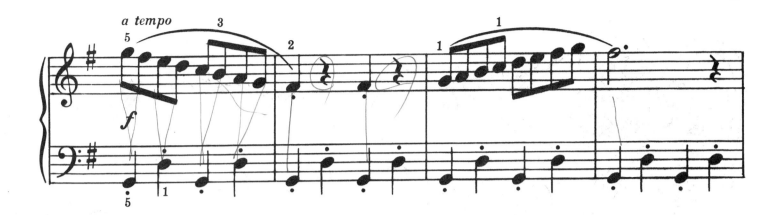

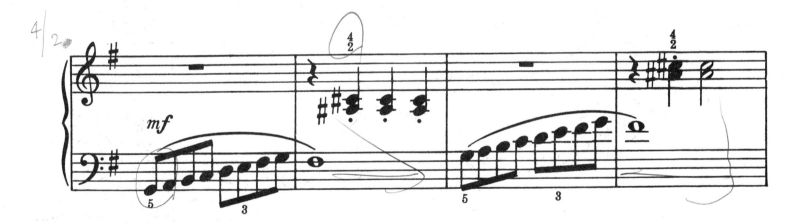

This Old Man

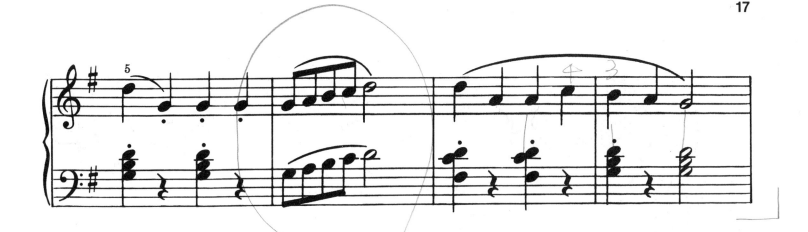

4/12

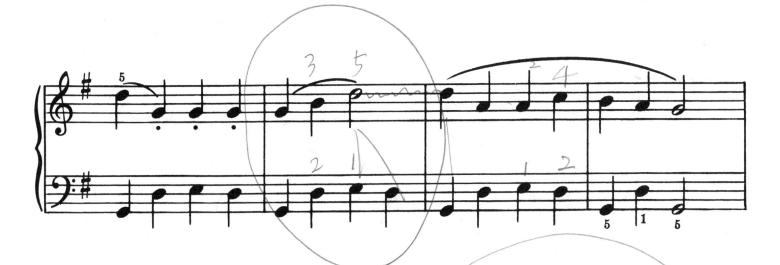

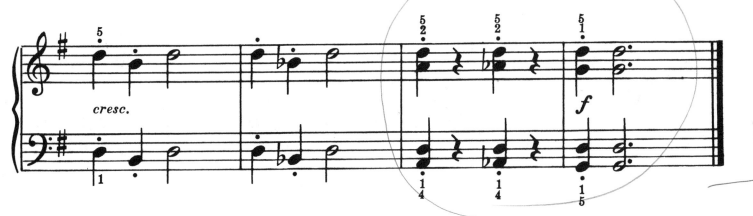

Tiger Chase

For He's a Jolly Good Fellow

Moderato

The Fly and the Bumblebee

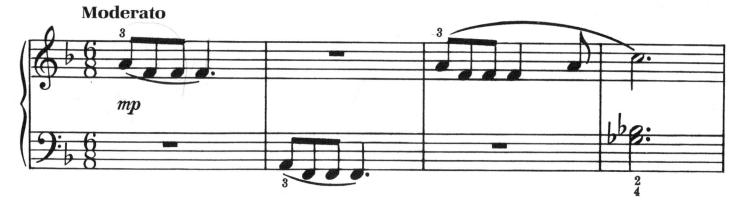

Fid-dle dee dee, Fid-dle dee dee, the fly has mar-ried the bum - ble bee.

Fid-dle dee dee, Fid-dle dee dee, the fly has mar-ried the bum-ble bee. The

fly said he, "Will you mar - ry me and live with me for - ev - er?"

Fid-dle dee dee, Fid-dle dee dee, the fly has mar-ried the bum - ble bee.

mf   *f*

Silver Bugles

Moderato

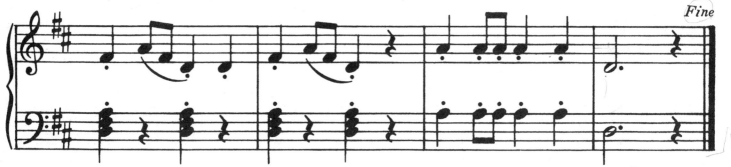

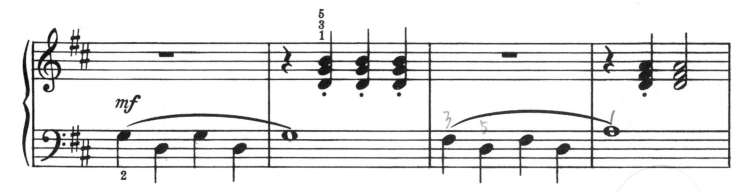

The King's Court

Steady march beat

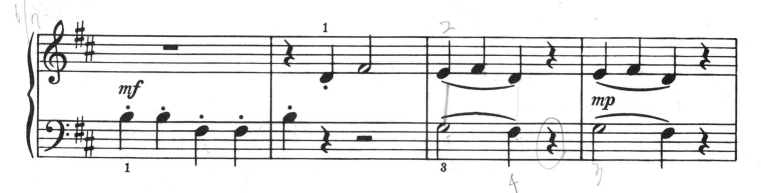

Use with page 41 of Piano, Level 2. **WP212**

Reindeer Rock

Fine

D.C. al Fine

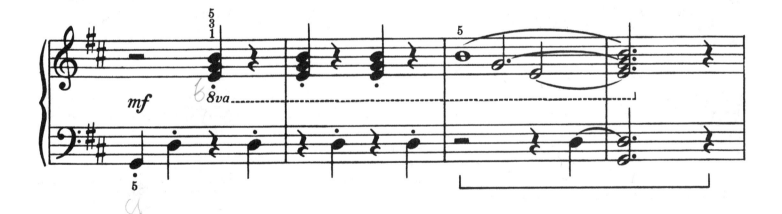

Flamenco Dancer

With spirit

a tempo

O - le!

8va..........

WP212

Moon Creatures

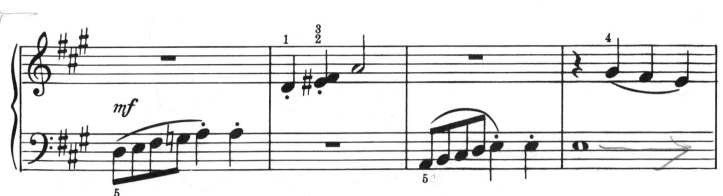

Square Dance Tune

With spirit

Rock Band

Fast rock beat

7/22